Validation

is a Practice

that grounds you

in the strength of

Who You Are

and nourishes your

whole being

I like
who I am

List all your qualities, gifts, passions

_____

_____

_____

_____

_____

_____

_____

This journal is designed for you
to validate your self for what you do well
and practice naming your feelings

These are two practices
from <u>Growing Up Whole: A Child's Guide Book</u>
that teaches you many healthy life skills to stay
connected and whole throughout your life's journey.

When you need to "bounce back" from something
hard, you can read your validation journals to yourself
to remind yourself who you are and all the things you
have done well in your life!

When I listen to my heart♡

I will know my truth
and the right actions to take

I will know Who I AM

and what my purpose is for being

and what gifts I have to share
with the world!

Emotions Are Like Leaves

Emotions are energy.

Emotions move and change.

Emotions are Messengers.

Emotions give me important information.

I can have many feelings at once.

What I did well today!

_____

_____

_____

Feelings I felt today:

_____

_____

_____

I want to Be
The best Me
I can Be

What I did well today!

_____

_____

_____

Feelings I felt today:

_____

_____

_____

I can name
and feel
all of
my feelings

What I did well today!

_____

_____

_____

Feelings I felt today:

_____

_____

_____

My Imagination
is a Treasure

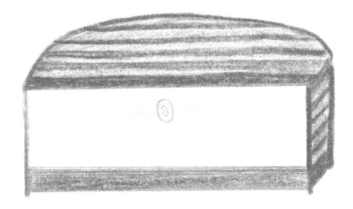

What I did well today!

_____

_____

_____

Feelings I felt today:

_____

_____

_____

Forgiveness
is a gift
I give to myself
and to others

I Forgive Myself for

I Forgive Others for.

What I did well today!

_____

_____

_____

I forgive myself for:

_____

_____

_____

I bounce back
when things are
hard

I Am

Resilient!

What I did well today!

_____

_____

_____

Feelings I felt today:

_____

_____

_____

My body
is the home of my Spirit

What I did well today!

_____

_____

_____

Healthy Things I do for my Body

_____

_____

_____

I am a part
of the Earth
and I care
about all
living things

What I did well today!

_____

_____

_____

Things I do to care for the earth

_____

_____

_____

The Golden Rule
reminds me to
treat others
the way
I want to be
treated.

What I did well today!

_____

_____

_____

How I want to be treated:

_____

_____

_____

I am
Creative

What I did well today!

_____

_____

_____

How I create:

_____

_____

_____

I feed my body
healthy food
water
and vitamins
to
grow strong

What I did well today!

_____

_____

_____

Healthy foods I ate today:

_____

_____

_____

I am
Compassionate

What I did well today!

_____

_____

_____

Feelings I felt today:

_____

_____

_____

I Am Loved
Loving
And
Loveable

What I did well today!

_____

_____

_____

Feelings I felt today:

_____

_____

_____

I Am
Brave!

What I did well today!

_____

_____

_____

Courageous things I have done in my life:

_____

_____

_____

I Am
Curious

What I did well today!

_____

_____

_____

Feelings I felt today:

_____

_____

_____

I Honor
My Hopes
and
My Dreams

What I did well today!

_____

_____

_____

I dream about:

_____

_____

_____

I Am
Honest

What I did well today!

_____

_____

_____

When I'm honest I feel:

_____

_____

_____

What I Say Matters

What I did well today!

_____

_____

_____

Feelings I felt today:

_____

_____

_____

I use enCOURAGing
Words to myself!

"I can!"

"I am doing the best
I can!"

"You tried very hard."

What I did well today!

_____

_____

_____

Feelings I felt today:

_____

_____

_____

I am
A
Good Friend

What I did well today!

_____

_____

_____

Things I do for my friends:

_____

_____

_____

I encourage
others by
saying nice things

"You can do it!"

"Well done"

What I did well today!

_____

_____

_____

Feelings I felt today:

_____

_____

_____

I Am Unique
and
so is Everyone Else

What I did well today!

_____

_____

_____

Feelings I felt today:

_____

_____

_____

I Am
Thoughtful
and
Care About
Others

What I did well today!

_____

_____

_____

Feelings I felt today:

_____

_____

_____

I Believe

In

Myself

What I did well today!

_____

_____

_____

Feelings I felt today:

_____

_____

_____

I Celebrate

and

Feel JOY

What I did well today!

_____

_____

_____

Feelings I felt today:

_____

_____

_____

I Follow
My
Inner Guidance

What I did well today!

_____

_____

_____

My heart wants to:

_____

_____

_____

I take time
to listen
to myself

What I did well today!

_____

_____

_____

Feelings I felt today:

_____

_____

_____

I take time
to listen
to others

What I did well today!

_____

_____

_____

Feelings I felt today:

_____

_____

_____

I Am Compassionate

What I did well today!

_____

_____

_____

Feelings I felt today:

_____

_____

_____

I Am
Strong and Bold

What I did well today!

_____

_____

_____

Feelings I felt today:

_____

_____

_____

I Love Myself

and

I Share My Love

With Others

What I did well today!

_____

_____

_____

Feelings I felt today:

_____

_____

_____

For inspirational books, music, growth charts

Visit us at www.GrowingUpWhole.com

Growing Up Whole

Printed in the United States. **Luna Madre™ Publishing**
3463 State Street, Suite 225, Santa Barbara CA 93105
www.LunaMadre.com   www.GrowingUpWhole.com

A Child's Validation Journal: Growing Up Whole™
ISBN: 978-0-9887724-3-4   Library of Congress # on file
Editor: Annie J. Dahlgren   Illustrations/Artwork: Linda Newlin
Graphic Design of Cover: Cecilia Martini Muth
CC Design, Santa Barbara CA

CPSIA information can be obtained
at www.ICGtesting.com
Printed in the USA
BVHW092034190519
548565BV00005B/26/P

9 780988 772434